SEASCAPE

Compiled by
R.H.C. Fice and Iris Simkiss

Macmillan

First published 1972 by
MACMILLAN EDUCATION LTD
Basingstoke and London
Companies and representatives throughout the world

Photoset by BAS Printers Limited, Wallop, Hampshire
Printed in Great Britain by A. Wheaton & Co., Exeter
Illustrated by Carol Lawson

CONTENTS

Sailing the wide sea

Birds, beasts and fishes

Under the water

ACKNOWLEDGEMENTS

The author and publishers wish to thank the following, who have kindly given permission for the use of copyright material: George Allen and Unwin and Rand McNally for an extract from *The Kon-Tiki Expedition* by Thor Heyerdahl; Barrie and Jenkins Limited for an extract from *Seascape* by Frances Cornford; The Bodley Head for extracts from *Tarka the Otter* by Henry Williamson; Chatto & Windus Limited for 'Fishing Harbour Towards Evening' from *Control Tower* by Richard Kell; Curtis Brown Limited (New York) for an extract from *Boy Blue's Book of Beasts* by W.J. Smith; J.M. Dent and Sons Ltd, for extracts from *Typhoon* and *Youth* by Joseph Conrad; Granada Publishing and Harcourt Brace and World Inc. for *Harpoon at a Venture* by Gavin Maxwell, 'maggie and milly and mollie and may' by e.e. cummings and 'The Dead Crab' from *Collected Poems* by Andrew Young; George G. Harrap and Company Limited for extract from *The Harrap Book of Sea Verse* by George Darley; David Higham Associates Limited for extract from *Sailor* by Eleanor Farjeon; Hamish Hamilton and Harper and Row, for extract from *The Silent World* by J.Y. Cousteau; William Heinemann Limited for 'The Sea' and 'Grim and Gloomy' from *The Wandering Moon* by James Reeves and 'The Giant Crab' from *The Truants* by John Walsh; Lutterworth Press for extract from *The Wheel on the School* by Meindert DeJong; Oxford University Press for *Beowulf The Warrior* and *Across the Pacific*, an extract from *The Ballad of Kon-Tiki* by Ian Serraillier, 'Sir Patrick Spens' from *Oxford Book of Poetry* compiled by Edward Blishen; Laurence Pollinger Limited for extract from *The Ship* by Richard Church (William Heinemann); Mr. E. V. Rieu for poem from *A Puffin Quartet of Poets*; Sidgewick and Jackson Limited for 'Fog' from *Vagabond Verses* by Crosbie Garstin; The Society of Authors as Literary Representative of the Estate of John Masefield for *Trade Winds* by John Masefield also The Literary Trustees of Walter de la Mare and The Society of Authors 'The Pool in the Rock' from *Complete Poems of Walter de la Mare* (1969); Miss M. Thomas for extract from *The Child on the Cliffs* by Edward Thomas; Thomas Nelson and Sons Ltd, Publishers for extract from *Westward Ho!* by Charles Kingsley; Mr. John Walsh for poem 'First Dip' from *The Roundabout by the Sea*; Mrs. George Bembridge and A. P. Watt and Son for 'A Smugglers Song' from *Puck of Pook's Hill* by Rudyard Kipling and Mr. Peter Newbolt for 'Drake's Drum' from *Poems Old and New* by Sir Henry Newbolt. Also Angus and Robertson Ltd for 'Cormorants' from *A Beachcomber's Diary* by John Blight.

BESIDE THE SEA

The Sea

The sea is a hungry dog,
Giant and grey.
He rolls on the beach all day.
With his clashing teeth and shaggy jaws

Hour upon hour he gnaws
The rumbling, tumbling stones,
And 'Bones, bones, bones, bones!'
The giant sea-dog moans,
Licking his greasy paws.

And when the night wind roars
And the moon rocks in the stormy cloud,
He bounds to his feet and snuffs and sniffs,
Shaking his wet sides over the cliffs,
And howls and hollos long and loud.

But on quiet days in May or June,
When even the grasses on the dune
Play no more their reedy tune,
With his head between his paws
He lies on the sandy shores,
So quiet, so quiet, he scarcely snores.

James Reeves

First Dip

Wave after wavelet goes
Coldly over your toes
And sinks down into the stones,
Another mounts to your knees,
Icy, as if to freeze
Flesh and marrow and bones.
And now another, a higher,
Yellow with foam, and dire
With weed from yesterday's storm.
With a gasp you greet it –
Your shoulders stoop to meet it –
And you find . . . you find . . .
    Ah-h-h-h!
You find that the water's warm.

John Walsh

maggie and milly and molly and may

maggie and milly and molly and may
went down to the beach (to play one day)

and maggie discovered a shell that sang
so sweetly she couldn't remember her troubles, and

milly befriended a stranded star
whose rays five languid fingers were;

and molly was chased by a horrible thing
which raced sideways while blowing bubbles: and

may came home with a smooth round stone
as small as a world and as large as alone.

For whatever we lose (like a you or a me)
it's always ourselves we find in the sea

e. e. cummings

The Old Boat

Slowly Lina crossed the dry strand, skirting the few
puddles left in hollow places from the last flood tide.
Even as quietly as Lina came, the heron heard her.
With a loud, disagreeable squawk it flapped up and
flew away over the dike. Lina was alone in the silent
dry stretches of the mysterious sea. Before her loomed
the dark old boat.

It was difficult to know how to climb to the top of
the high, round-bottomed fishing boat. Why she
wanted to get on the boat, Lina didn't exactly know;
except that now she was here, it seemed she had to do
something. She couldn't just walk around it and walk
back to sit on the dike! The whole boat looked

slippery and slimy with seaweed and sea scum. It was crusted all over with strange rotted growths. Big crabs scurried under the boat. It was so still here Lina could hear the scuttling, clicking movements of the hard-shell crabs. Snails and other slow slimy sea animals clung and moved everywhere among the weeds and rotted wood.

Lina walked around the boat once again. There was only one way to get up on it. An old anchor chain still hung at the stern. It was as coated and slimy as all the rest. If she clung to the chain and pulled herself up by it, she could sort of walk up the rounded stern – if she took her wooden shoes off.

Lina considered. She really should take her socks and stockings off, too, but the thought of climbing the crusted boat, with her bare toes among the slime and scum and moving things, gave her cold horror. She'd just take her shoes off. But when she set her shoes on the dry sea bottom, they looked so tiny and helpless and out of place in the big sea that Lina felt wretched. She couldn't leave them behind.

On sudden impulse Lina pulled the ribbon out of her hair, strung it through two holes in the sides of her wooden shoes, and hung the shoes around her neck by the ribbon. Then shutting her eyes tight, she grabbed the coated chain and, bracing her feet flat against the stern of the boat, hoisted herself up.

From *The Wheel on the School*
Meindert DeJong

Boats at Night

How lovely is the sound of oars at night,
And unknown voices, borne through the windless air,
From shadowy vessels floating out of sight
Beyond the harbour lantern's broken glare,
To those piled rocks that make on the dark wave
Only a darker stain. The splashing oars
Slide softly on as in an echoing cave
And with a whisper of the unseen shores
Mingle their music, till the bell of night
Murmurs reverberations low and deep,
That droop towards the land in swooning flight.
Like whispers from the lazy lips of sleep
The oars grow faint. Below the cloud-dim hill
The shadows fade, and now the bay is still.

Edward Shanks

The Harbour

There Amyas sat a full half-hour, and glanced at
whiles from Frank to look upon the scene around.
Outside the south-west wind blew fresh and strong,
and the moonlight danced upon a thousand crests of
foam; but within the black jagged point which
sheltered the town the sea did but heave, in long oily
swells of rolling silver, onward into the black shadow
of the hills, within which the town and pier lay
invisible, save where a twinkling light gave token of
some lonely fisher's wife, watching the weary night
through for the boat which would return with dawn.

From *Westward Ho!*
Charles Kingsley

The Child on the Cliffs

Mother, the root of this little yellow flower
Among the stones has the taste of quinine.
Things are strange to-day on the cliff. The sun
  shines so bright,
And the grasshopper works at his sewing-machine
So hard. Here's one on my hand, mother, look;
I lie so still. There's one on your book.

12

But I have something to tell more strange. So leave
Your book to the grasshopper, mother dear, –
Like a green knight in a dazzling market-place, –
And listen now. Can you hear what I hear
Far out? Now and then the foam there curls
And stretches a white arm out like a girl's.

Fishes and gulls ring no bells. There cannot be
A chapel or church between here and Devon,
With fishes or gulls ringing its bell, – hark! –
Somewhere under the sea or up in heaven.
'It's the bell, my son, out in the bay
On the buoy. It does sound sweet to-day.'

Sweeter I never heard, mother, no, not in all Wales.
I should like to be lying under that foam,
Dead, but able to hear the sound of the bell,
And certain that you would often come
And rest, listening happily.
I should be happy if that could be.

Edward Thomas

The Storm

I reached the rocks at the side of the bay, eyes shut and bent double. Here the noise of the sea was stupefying. Over the reefs and isolated rocks a little to the north the sea had lost all form and architecture; here was no articulated procession of rollers, but a tumbling, leaping, white confusion, out of which shot up every now and again a column like a single vigorous puff from a big steam engine. Further off the rollers were in vast and orderly ranks, thirty feet high and lead-grey, with the white spume snarling back from them; the gradual, terrible piling up of force before each crest curled over and the whole ridge of water came roaring down in collapse. I turned to look at the big cliff to the north, and watched as again and again it was hidden by a mighty white mushroom of close-packed spray.

From *Harpoon at a Venture*
Gavin Maxwell

Seascape

The liquid unhorizoned sea
Heaves tranquilly,
As though
Inshore below,
How few feet deep,
A lazy mermaid turned herself in sleep.
That boy, entranced, who quite forgets his spade
To stand and stare,
Might almost wade
And peering find his ankles in her seaweed hair.
But he would rather watch his cork afloat,
Lulled on the lucent, calm expanse above,
Or see the far-off chuffing motor boat
As white as Noah's dove.

Frances Cornford

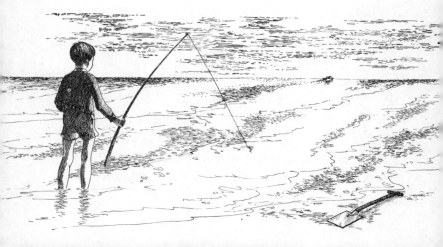

A mermaiden

Chilled with salt dew, tossed on dark waters deep,
Sailors and fishers loved her in their sleep,
And not a few would wed her in their dreams!

  Yet when, within their net, one autumn night
They felt and dragged her sliding weight, it seems
Star-sprinkled skies and phosphorescent light
On all the billows' tops, and on the net
Making a spider's-mesh of sparkles bright,
Dripping like pearls off her curled horse-tail hair –
Low-breathed they haul, and dunch! she's on the
    planks all right.

  What may be done with her can no man fathom,
    yet
Pretty as paint she starts, but tails so awkwardly.
Nor any of the crew will wish or dare
To take her home and, for their very lives,
To face again their daughters and their wives.

  No fishing-clouts will fit her quite, and all in vain
They put her out fried mackerel and hot tea.
Says one, 'Things being a turn of year
'We'll take ashore the maid, and at the church
'Of Lanteglos-by-Fowey, being near –
'Along with pilchards, breams, and perch,
Fruit, turnips, autumn-flowers and marrows
'Which ornament the choir-stalls, piers, and rails

'And openings of pulpit narrow,
'Put her in window for the Harvest Show!'

   '—Though folk will have to mind her dripping tails
'Upon their bonnets, hymn-books, shawls, and pews.
'I'll hurry to the Rector with the news,
'And just remark, "Look here, sir, what we've
      found!
' "Are we to drop her back, or in a tank
' "Send her along to the Aquarium?" '
'O-ho!' some others cried,
'We'll run her up the High Street in a barrow.'

   An elder stroked his chin, and drank some rum
From wickered bottle: 'Nay, for did we so,
'Being a witch, she'd visit us with woe;
'Or nightmares foul, or other sort of itch –
'She, or some kindred doubtful spirit dumb!
'—She weeps, and calls her lover, but in vain,
'These sea-maids marry none but sailors drowned,
'Fetch wind-spouts, or bring whirlpools in a calm!'

With this, he smites one crab-fist down in palm,
'I'll just say what, we'll simply scrag the witch!
'And in the cauldron used for melting pitch
'Boil down the tail-end: she is every sailor's foe
'And simply lures poor duffers to their fate.
'The rest we'll cut in lumps and use for bait.'

On this, the boatswain rather sternly spoke:
'Friend, what you say goes farther than a joke.
' 'Twas honest counsel beyond any doubt,
'Yet did the parish constable find out,
'He and the clergyman would call it guilt:
'So might for her cold blood thy hot be spilt!''

So then a more religious gave his mind:
' 'Twould be temptation to the village boys
'And frighten half the maids, if they should find
'That ladies such as this should be,

'Who may betroth the dead, or with a spirit
'Vex us, and what our children may inherit:
'And bring about, perhaps, our total loss.
'We, being Christians, needs must sink her with the
    cross.'

And so with spars and ropes they made her fast
And with the anchor sank. There, fathoms deep,
She found the sandy bottom, so for aye to sleep.
    Later near by they hung a passing bell
Hard by a charted rock: which tolls the rising swell.

Thomas Hennell

SAILORS, SMUGGLERS AND PIRATES

The Smuggler

O my true love's a smuggler and sails upon the sea;
I wish I were a smuggler to go along with he;
To go along with he for the satins and the wine,
And run the tubs at Slapton when the stars do shine.

O Hollands is a good drink when the nights are cold,
And Brandy is a good drink for them as are growing
   old.
There are lights up in the cliff-tops when the boats
   are homeward-bound,
And we run the tubs at Slapton when the word goes
   round.

The King he is a fine man in his bright red coat,
But I do love a smuggler in his little fishing-boat;
He runs the Mallins lace and he spends his money
   free,
And I would I were a smuggler to go along with he.

Anonymous

19

A Smuggler's Song

If you wake at midnight, and hear a horse's feet,
Don't go drawing back the blind, or looking in
   the street,
Them that ask no questions isn't told a lie.
Watch the wall, my darling, while the Gentlemen
   go by!

      Five and twenty ponies,
      Trotting through the dark –
      Brandy for the Parson,
      'Baccy for the Clerk;
Laces for a lady; letters for a spy,
And watch the wall, my darling, while the Gentlemen
   go by!

Running round the woodlump if you chance to find
Little barrels, roped and tarred, all full of brandy-
   wine,
Don't you shout to come and look, nor use em
   for your play,
Put the brushwood back again, – and they'll be gone
   next day!

If you see the stable-door setting open wide;
If you see a tired horse lying down inside;
If your mother mends a coat cut about and tore;
If the lining's wet and warm – don't you ask
   no more!

If you meet King George's men, dressed in blue
and red,
You be careful what you say, and mindful what is
said.
If they call you 'pretty maid', and chuck you 'neath
the chin,
Don't you tell where no one is, nor yet where
no one's been!

Knocks and footsteps round the house – whistles
after dark –
You've no call for running out till the house-dogs
bark.
Trusty's here, and *Pincher's* here, and see how dumb
they lie –
They don't fret to follow when the Gentlemen go by!

If you do as you've been told, 'likely there's a
chance,
You'll be give a dainty doll, all the way from France,
With a cap of Valenciennes, and a velvet hood –
A present from the Gentlemen, along o' being good!

> Five and twenty ponies,
> Trotting through the dark –
> Brandy for the Parson,
> 'Baccy for the Clerk.

Them that asks no questions isn't told a lie –
Watch the wall, my darling, while the Gentlemen
go by!

Rudyard Kipling

Pirate Don Durk of Dowdee

Ho, for the Pirate Don Durk of Dowdee!
He was as wicked as wicked could be,
But oh, he was perfectly gorgeous to see!
　　The Pirate Don Durk of Dowdee.

His conscience, of course, was as black as a bat,
But he had a floppety plume on his hat
And when he went walking it jiggled – like that!
　　The plume of the Pirate Dowdee.

His coat it was crimson and cut with a slash,
And often as ever he twirled his moustache,
Deep down in the ocean the mermaids went splash,
　　Because of Don Durk of Dowdee.

Moreover, Dowdee had a purple tattoo,
And stuck in his belt where he buckled it through
Were a dagger, a dirk and a squizzamaroo
　　For fierce was the Pirate Dowdee.

So fearful he was he would shoot at a puff,
And always at sea when the weather grew rough
He drank from a bottle and wrote on his cuff,
   Did Pirate Don Durk of Dowdee.

Oh, he had a cutlass that swung at his thigh
And he had a parrot called Pepperkin Pye,
And a zigzaggy scar at the end of his eye
   Had Pirate Don Durk of Dowdee.

He kept in a cavern, this buccaneer bold,
A curious chest that was covered with mould,
And all of his pockets were jingly with gold!
   Oh jing! went the gold of Dowdee.

His conscience, of course, it was crook'd like a
   squash,
But both of his boots made a slickery slosh,
And he went through the world with a wonderful
   swash,
   Did Pirate Don Durk of Dowdee.

It's true he was wicked as wicked could be,
His sins they outnumbered a hundred and three,
But oh, he was perfectly gorgeous to see,
   The Pirate Don Durk of Dowdee.

Mildred Meigs

Sailor

My sweetheart's a Sailor,
He sails on the sea,
When he comes home
He brings presents for me;
Coral from China,
Silks from Siam,
Parrots and pearls
From Seringapatam,
Silver from Mexico,
Gold from Peru,
Indian feathers
From Kalamazoo,
Scents from Sumatra,
Mantillas from Spain,
A fisherman's float
From the waters of Maine,
Reindeers from Lapland,
Ducks from Bombay,
A unicorn's horn
From the Land of Cathay –
Isn't it lucky
For someone like me
To marry a Sailor
Who sails on the sea!

Eleanor Farjeon

Long John Silver

We made a curious figure, had any one been there
to see us; all in soiled sailor clothes, and all but me
armed to the teeth. Silver had two guns slung about
him – one before and one behind – besides the great
cutlass at his waist, and a pistol in each pocket of his
square-tailed coat. To complete his strange appear-
ance, Captain Flint sat perched upon his shoulder and
gabbled odds and ends of purposeless sea-talk. I had
a line about my waist, and followed obediently after
the sea-cook, who held the loose end of the rope, now
in his free hand, now between his powerful teeth. For
all the world, I was led like a dancing bear.

From *Treasure Island*
R. L. Stevenson

Sir Patrick Spens

1. The Sailing

The king sits in Dunfermline town,
    Drinking the blude-red wine;
"O whar will I get a skeely skipper
    To sail this new ship o' mine?"

Up and spak an eldern knight,
    Sat at the king's right knee:
"Sir Patrick Spens is the best sailor
    That ever sail'd the sea."

Our king has written a braid letter,
    And seal'd it wi' his hand,
And sent it to Sir Patrick Spens,
    Was walking on the strand.

"To Noroway, to Noroway,
    To Noroway o'er the faem;
The king's daughter o' Noroway,
    'Tis thou maun bring her hame."

The first word that Sir Patrick read
    A loud laugh laughed he;
The neist word that Sir Patrick read,
    The tear blinded his e'e.

"Oh wha is this has done this deed
  And tauld the king o' me,
To send us out, at this time o' year,
  To sail upon the sea?

"Be it wind, be it weet, be it hail, be it sleet,
  Our ship must sail the faem;
The king's daughter o' Noroway,
  'Tis we maun fetch her hame."

They hoysed their sails on Monenday morn
  Wi' a' the speed they may;
The ha'e landed in Noroway
  Upon a Wodensday.

2. The Return

"Mak ready, mak ready, my merry men a'!
    Our gude ship sails the morn." –
Now ever alack, my master dear,
    I fear a deadly storm!"

"I saw the new moon late yestreen
    Wi' the auld moon in her arm;
And if we gang to sea, master,
    I fear we'll come to harm!"

They hadna' sailed a league, a league,
    A league but barely three,
When the lift grew dark, and the wind blew loud,
    And gurly grew the sea.

The anchors brak, and the topmast lap
    It was sic a deadly storm;
And the waves cam owre the broken ship
    Till a' her sides were torn.

"O whar will I get a gude sailor
    To tak my helm in hand,
Till I get up to the tall topmast
    To see if I can spy land?"

"Oh here am I, a sailor gude,
   To tak the helm in hand,
Till you go up to the tall topmast,
   But I fear you'll ne'er spy land."

He hadna gane a step, a step,
   A step but barely ane,
When a bolt flew out of our goodly ship,
   And the saut sea it came in.

"Gae fetch a web o' the silken claith,
   Another o' the twine,
And wap them into our ship's side,
   And let na' the sea come in."

They fetched a web o' the silken claith,
   Another o' the twine,
And they wrapped them round that gude ship's side,
   But still the sea cam in.

O laith, laith were our gude Scots lords
   To wet their cork-heel'd shoon;
But lang or a' the play was play'd
   They wet their hats aboon.

And mony was the feather bed
   That flatter'd on the faem;
And mony was the gude laird's son
   That never mair cam hame.

O lang, lang may the ladies sit,
   Wi' their fans into their hand,
Before they see Sir Patrick Spens
   Come sailing to the strand!

And lang, lang may the maidens sit
   Wi' their gowd kames in their hair,
A' waiting for their ain dear loves!
   For them they'll see nae mair.

Half-owre, half-owre to Aberdour,
   'Tis fifty fathoms deep;
And there lies gude Sir Patrick Spens
   Wi' the Scots lords at his feet!

               Anonymous

Drake's Drum

Drake he's in his hammock an' a thousand mile
   away
   (Capten, art tha sleepin' there below?),
Slung atween the round shot in Nombre Dios Bay,
   An' dreamin' arl the time o' Plymouth Hoe.

Yarnder lumes the Island, yarnder lie the ships,
    Wi' sailor lads a dancin' heel-an'-toe,
An' the shore-lights flashin', an' the night-tide
    dashin',
    He sees et arl so plainly as he saw et long ago.

Drake he was a Devon man, an' ruled the Devon
    seas,
    (Capten, art tha sleepin' there below?)
Rovin' tho' his death fell, he went wi' heart at ease,
    An' dreamin' arl the time o' Plymouth Hoe.
'Take my drum to England, hang et by the shore,
    Strike et when your powder's runnin' low;
If the Dons sight Devon, I'll quit the port o' Heaven,
    An' drum them up the Channel as we drummed
        them long ago.'

Drake he's in his hammock till the great Armadas
    come,
    (Capten, art tha sleepin' there below?)
Slung atween the round shot, listenin' for the drum,
    An' dreamin' arl the time o' Plymouth Hoe.
Call him on the deep sea, call him up the Sound,
    Call him when ye sail to meet the foe;
Where the old trade's plyin' an' the old flag flyin'
    They shall find him ware an' wakin', as they found
        him long ago!

Sir Henry Newbolt

Psalm 107

They that go down to the sea in ships, that do
    business in great waters;
These see the works of the Lord, and his wonders in
    the deep.
For he commandeth, and raiseth the stormy wind,
    which lifteth up the waves thereof.
They mount up to the heaven, they go down again to
    the depths: their soul is melted because of trouble.
They reel to and fro, and stagger like a drunken
    man, and are at their wits' end.
Then they cry unto the Lord in their trouble, and he
    bringeth them out of their distresses.
He maketh the storm a calm, so that the waves
    thereof are still.
Then they are glad because they be quiet; so he
    bringeth them unto their desired haven.

SAILING THE WIDE SEA

The Ship

They have launched the little ship,
She is riding by the quay.
Like a young doe to the river,
She has trembled to the sea.

Her sails are shaken loose;
They flutter in the wind.
The cat-paws ripple round her
And the gulls scream behind.

The rope is cast, she moves
Daintily out and south,
Where the snarling ocean waits her
With tiger-foaming mouth.

Richard Church

Trade Winds

In the harbour, in the island, in the Spanish Seas,
Are the tiny white houses and the orange-trees,
And day-long, night-long, the cool and pleasant breeze
    Of the steady Trade Winds blowing.

There is the red wine, the nutty Spanish ale,
The shuffle of the dancers, the old salt's tale,
The squeaking fiddle, and the soughing in the sail
    Of the steady Trade Winds blowing.

And o' nights there's fire-flies and the yellow moon,
And in the ghostly palm-trees the sleepy tune
Of the quiet voice calling me, the long low croon
    Of the steady Trade Winds blowing.

John Masefield

Typhoon

The motion of the ship was extravagant. Her
lurches had an appalling helplessness: she pitched as
if taking a header into a void, and seemed to find a
wall to hit every time. When she rolled she fell on her
side headlong, and she would be righted back by such
a demolishing blow that Jukes felt her reeling as a
clubbed man reels before he collapses. The gale

howled and scuffled about gigantically in the darkness, as though the entire world were one black gully. At certain moments the air streamed against the ship as if sucked through a tunnel with a concentrated solid force of impact that seemed to lift her clean out of the water and keep her up for an instant with only a quiver running through her from end to end. And then she would begin her tumbling again as if dropped back into a boiling cauldron . . .

. . . her middle structure was like a half-tide rock awash upon a coast. It was like an outlying rock with the water boiling up, streaming over, pouring off, beating round – like a rock in the surf to which ship-wrecked people cling before they let go – only it rose, it sank, it rolled continuously, without respite and rest, like a rock that should have miraculously struck adrift from a coast and gone wallowing upon the sea.

The *Nan-Shan* was being looted by the storm with a senseless, destructive fury: trysails torn out of the extra gaskets, double-lashed awnings blown away, bridge swept clean, weathercloths burst, rails twisted, light-screens smashed – and two of the boats gone already. They had gone unheard and unseen, melting, as it were, in the shock and smother of the wave.

From *Typhoon*
Joseph Conrad

Fog

Over the oily swell it heaved, it rolled,
Like some foul creature, filmy, nebulous.
It pushed out streaming tentacles, took clammy hold,
Swaddled the spars, wrapped us in damp and cold,
Blotted the sun, crept round and over us.

Day long, night long, it hid us from the sky –
Hid us from sun and stars as in a tomb.
Shrouded in mist a berg went groaning by.
Far and forlorn we heard the blind ships cry,
Like lost souls wailing in a hopeless gloom.

Like a bell-wether clanging from the fold,
A codder called her dories. With scared breath
The steamer sirens shrieked; and mad bells tolled.
Through time eternal in the dark we rolled
Playing a game of Blind-Man's-Buff with Death.

Crosbie Garstin

The Main-Deep

The long-rólling,
Steady-póuring,
Deep-trenchéd
Green billów:

The wide-topped,
Unbróken,
Green-glacid,
Slow-sliding,

Cold-flushing,
– On – on – on –
Chill-rushing,
Hush – hushing,

. . . Hush – hushing . . .

James Stephens

Ice

And now there came both mist and snow,
And it grew wondrous cold:
And ice, mast high, came floating by,
As green as emerald.

And through the drifts the snowy clifts
Did send a dismal sheen:
Nor shapes of men nor beasts we ken –
The ice was all between.

The ice was here, the ice was there,
The ice was all around:
It crack'd and growl'd, and roar'd and howl'd,
Like noises in a swound!

From *The Rime of the Ancient Mariner*
Samuel Taylor Coleridge

The Whale Shark

Knut had been squatting there, washing his pants
in the swell, and when he looked up for a moment he
was staring straight into the biggest and ugliest face
any of us had ever seen in the whole of our lives. It
was the head of a veritable sea monster, so huge and
so hideous that if the Old Man of the Sea himself had
come up he could not have made such an impression
on us. The head was broad and flat like a frog's, with
two small eyes right at the sides, and a toadlike jaw
which was four or five feet wide and had long fringes
hanging drooping from the corners of the mouth.
Behind the head was an enormous body ending in
a long thin tail with a pointed tail fin which stood
straight up and showed that this sea monster was not
any kind of whale. The body looked brownish under
the water, but both head and body were thickly
covered with small white spots. The monster came

quietly, lazily swimming after us from astern. It grinned like a bulldog and lashed gently with its tail. The large round dorsal fin projected clear of the water and sometimes the tail fin as well, and when the creature was in the trough of the swell the water flowed about the broad back as though washing around a submerged reef. In front of the broad jaws swam a whole crowd of zebra-striped pilot fish in fan formation, and large remora fish and other parasites sat firmly attached to the huge body and travelled with it through the water, so that the whole thing looked like a curious zoological collection crowded round something that resembled a floating deep water reef.

From *The Kon-Tiki Expedition*
Thor Heyerdahl

Across the Pacific

They were not lonely. They found the sea
No barren waste but a living world,
Peopled as the woodland with wild creatures,
Curious and shy. The rough-riding steamer
With his foaming prow and his engine roar
Sees them not. But Kon-Tiki scared them not away.

As timid birds at twilight hop and twitter
On the summer lawn about the quiet house,
So now about the noiseless floating raft
The frolicking sea-dwellers. Then did Ocean,
The great showman, out of the bountiful deep
Conjure all manner of strange creatures
To delight them: flying fish that shot through the air
Like quicksilver, smack against the sail,
Then dropped to deck into the breakfast saucepan
Waiting there; the prosperous tunny,
Fat as an alderman with rows of double chins;

The glorious dolphin, bluebottle-green
With glittering golden fins, greedy
For the succulent weed that trailed like garlands
From the steering oar. There were many more –
Take the blue shark, a glutton
For blood; he'd swallow a dolphin, bones and all,
And crunch them like a concrete-mixer. They learnt
How to fool him with tit-bits, to get him
By his tail and haul aboard, skipping

Quickly from the snapping jaw –
He'd make a meal of anyone who let him!
(Rare sport this for the parrot who
For safety flew to the roof of the raft
And shrieked at the fun of it and laughed and
    laughed.)
Every kind they saw, from the million pilot fish
Tiny as a finger nail
To the majestic tremendous spotted whale,
Long as a tennis-court, who could –
Were he so minded – with one flick of his great tail
Have swatted them flat as a fly. But he couldn't be
    bothered.
Instead, circling cumbrously below,
He scratched his lazy back on the steering oar,
Till Erik sent him packing
With half a foot of steel in his spine.
Deep down he plunged, and the harpoon line –
Whipping through their hands – snapped like twine.

From *The Ballad of the Kon-Tiki*
Ian Serrailler

Hunting Moby Dick, the White Whale

The triumphant halloo of thirty buckskin lungs was heard, as – Moby Dick bodily burst into view! For not by any calm and indolent spoutings; not by the peaceable gush of that mystic fountain in his head, did the White Whale now reveal his vicinity; but by the far more wondrous phenomen of breaching. Rising with his utmost velocity from the furthest depths, the Sperm Whale thus booms his entire bulk into the pure element of air, and piling up a mountain of dazzling foam, shows his place to the distance of seven miles and more. In those moments, the torn enraged waves he shakes off seem his mane; in some cases this breaching is his act of defiance.

'There she breaches! there she breaches!' was the cry, as in his immeasurable bravadoes the White Whale tossed himself salmon-like to Heaven. So suddenly seen in the blue plain of the sea, and relieved against the still bluer margin of the sky, the spray that he raised, for the moment, intolerably glittered and glared like a glacier; and stood there gradually fading and fading away from its first sparkling intensity, to the dim mistiness of an advancing shower in a vale.

'Aye, breach your last to the sun, Moby Dick!' cried Ahab, 'thy hour and thy harpoon are at hand!'

From *Moby Dick*
Herman Melville

Beowulf and his Warriors Return

When the Danes had shoved her
Clear of the shingle, the warriors leapt aboard.
They ran up the white sail. And the wind caught her,
The biting wind whipped her over the waves.
With timbers groaning, her curved prow scattering
    the foam,
Like a strong bird the swan-boat winged her way
Over the grey Baltic, the wintry whale-road,
Over the long paths of the ocean, on
And ever onward,
Till at last they beheld the shining cliffs of home.
The coastguard, spent with long weary watching,
Hailed them from afar. The keel struck the sand.
Proud, exultant, the warriors leapt to land.

From *Beowulf the Warrior*
Ian Serraillier

43

The Norse Coursers

O'er the wild gannet's bath
Come the Norse coursers!
O'er the whale's heritance
Gloriously steering!
With beaked heads peering,
Deep-plunging, high-rearing,
Tossing their foam abroad,
Shaking white manes aloft,
Creamy-necked, pitchy-ribbed,
Steeds of the Ocean!

O'er the Sun's mirror green
Come the Norse coursers!
Trampling its glassy breadth
Into bright fragments!
Hollow-backed, huge-bosomed,
Fraught with mailed riders,
Clanging with hauberks,
Shield, spear, and battleaxe,
Canvas-winged, cable-reigned,
Steeds of the Ocean!

O'er the Wind's ploughing-field
Come the Norse coursers!
By a hundred each ridden,
To the bloody feast bidden,
They rush in their fierceness
And ravine all around them!
Their shoulders enriching
With fleecy-light plunder,
Fire-spreading, foe-spurning,
Steeds of the Ocean!

George Darley

The Death of the Old Ship

And so the boats drifted about that night, heaving and setting on the swell. The men dozed, waked, sighed, groaned. I looked at the burning ship.

Between the darkness of earth and heaven she was burning fiercely upon a disc of purple sea shot by the blood-red play of gleams; upon a disc of water glittering and sinister. A high, clear flame, an immense and lonely flame, ascended from the ocean, and from its summit the black smoke poured continuously at the sky. She burned furiously, mournful and imposing like a funeral pile kindled in the night, surrounded by the sea, watched over by the stars. A magnificent death had come like a grace, like a gift, like a reward to that old ship at the end of her laborious days. The surrender of her weary ghost to the keeping of stars and sea was stirring like the sight of a glorious triumph. The masts fell just before daybreak, and for a moment there was a burst and turmoil of sparks that seemed to fill with flying fire the night patient and watchful, the vast night lying silent upon the sea. At daylight she was only a charred shell, floating still under a cloud of smoke and bearing a glowing mass of coal within.

Then the oars were got out, and the boats forming in a line moved round her remains as if in procession – the long-boat leading. As we pulled across her stern a slim dart of fire shot out viciously at us, and suddenly she went down, head first, in a great hiss of steam. The unconsumed stern was the last to sink; but the paint had gone, had cracked, had peeled off, and there were no letters, there was no word, no stubborn device that was like her soul, to flash at the rising sun her creed and her name.

From *Youth*
Joseph Conrad

BIRDS, BEASTS AND FISHES

The Albatross and the Equator

'Albatross, Albatross, why do you fly
Under my blue equatorial sky?
Albatross, Albatross, why do you roam
So far from your icy delectable home?'

'Capricorn warned me to turn to the right,
But I strayed from my course in the dead of the night
And the stars of the tropics, so many and new,
Led me by long ways and weary to you.'

The kindly Equator arose with a yawn
To the green and gold of the tropical dawn.
He called his Leviathans, little and large,
And handed the Albatross into their charge.

And he said to his Porpoises: 'Cease from your play,
And listen to me for the rest of the day:
I never have seen and seldom have heard
Of such an amazingly beautiful bird.

'She has flown from the far impossible South,
And strange are the sounds that come out of her
    mouth;
But the white of her breast and the spread of her
    wings
Are both surpassingly wonderful things.'

So they crowned her with seaweed Queen of the
    Birds
And humbly addressed her with flattering words;
And they gave her oysters and elegant fish
Daintily served on an amethyst dish.

They gave her a coral isle set in the calms
With a long white beach of coconut palms.
'Deign with your delicate feet,' said they,
'To tread this shade in the heat of the day.'

But the Albatross smiled with a tear in her heart,
As she said: 'I will walk for a little apart.'
And she paced by the echoing ocean alone,
Crooning a sorrowful song of her own:

'Fair are the tropical seas in the noon,
And fair in the glistening path of the moon.
But, oh, dearer to me are the storms of the Horn
Where the grey world-wandering waves are born.'

One moment they saw her, the next she had fled
Like a dream in the dawn or a shaft that is sped;
And all that she left on that desolate strand
Was the print of her foot and a tear in the sand.

She flew through the day and she flew through the
    night
With a heart that was bursting with hope and delight,
As the changing horizons came up with a swing
And the long leagues of ocean slipped under her
    wing –

Into the far incredible South,
Till she tasted the smell of the snow in her mouth,
And fluttered to rest in the land of her birth
On the ice that envelops the ends of the Earth.

E. V. Rieu

The Giant Crab

Along the steep wall at the old pier's side,
The scavenging crabs come up with the tide.
'Want to catch one? It's easy! You don't need a
    thing
But a stone, and some fish, and some odd bits of
    string;
Look here now – I'll show you. First fetch that big
    stone –
The one with the hole through – the cobble-shaped
    one;
Now join up your string – all the odd bits you've
    got –
Loop one end through the stone, and tie tight in a
    knot;
Then cram in these bits of stale fish for a bait . . .
Ready? Over she goes!
                          Now you've only to wait!'
Not long!

There's a tiny commotion below in the water;
There's a shout from above as the line becomes
    tauter;
There's a hauling up, hand over hand, until –
    whee-ee-ee! –
A monster-great crab swings clear of the sea –
All legs and sharp claws, hanging desperately on,
His pincers stuck fast through the hole in the stone!

'Quick get him!' 'No hurry! He's stupid – he'll cling
Till we land him. Pull steady, and don't break the
    string . . .
Whoops! Over he comes! Give the string a sharp
    shake,
And he'll let go his hold and fall down on his back.'

Well done!

'Now who'll pick him up?' 'Not me!' 'No, not me!
It's you said you fancied crab for your tea!'
'I said? I don't want him!' 'Hey, Billy, he's yours!
Come along and make friends with him!'
'What? With those claws?
I'm not touching him yet; I'll wait till he's dead!'
'You boil them alive; that's what my mother said;
They scream in the saucepan.' 'This one would get
    out:
He'd flop to the floor and go scrambling about –
He'd crawl on the baby; he'd frighten the cat;
Why, he could do anything with claws like that!
He could jab you –'
                'Hey, somebody! Lend me that stick:
Hook him by the legs and pitch him back quick!'

Whe-e-e-e-ew! Sploosh! He's gone! . . .

Thank goodness!

John Walsh

The Dead Crab

A rosy shield upon its back,
That not the hardest storm could crack,
From whose sharp edge projected out
Black pin-point eyes staring about;
Beneath, the well-knit cote-armure
That gave to its weak belly power;
The clustered legs with plated joints
That ended in stiletto points;
The claws like mouths it held outside:-
I cannot think this creature died
By storm or fish or sea-fowl harmed
Walking the sea so heavily armed;
Or does it make for death to be
Oneself a living armoury?

Andrew Young

Tarka Catches a Swan

While the pallor of the day was fading off the snow
a skein of great white birds, flying with arched wings
and long stretched necks, appeared with a measured
beat of pinions from the north and west. *Hompa*,
hompa, *hompa*, high in the cold air. Greymuzzle and
Tarka were eating seaweed and shellfish on the Sharshook, but when the swans splashed into the estuary,

they slipped into the tideway and drifted with the flow to where the wild swans were floating . . .

The beams of the lighthouse spread like the wings of a starfly above the level and sombre sands. Across the dark ridge of the Sharshook a crooked line of lamps winked below the hill. In one of the taverns a sailor was singing a shanty, the tune of which came distinctly over the Pool. The swans moved up with the tide, the otters after them. They were thin and weak; for mussels, winkles, and sometimes a sour green crab were poor nourishment for an otter who, in careless times, had eaten a three-pound sea-trout at a sitting and been hungry two hours afterwards.

The tide beyond the tail of the Sharshook was divided by a string of froth made by the leap and chop of waters beginning to move north and south, along the arms of the sea stretching to the Two Rivers. The swans turned north, borne by the tide racing past Crow Island. They paddled out of the main flow and turning head to tide, began to feed in the shallow over a sandbank. The otters drifted nearer, only their wide nostrils above water. When they were ten yards away from the nearest swan the nostrils sank, and chains of bubbles rose unseen above them. A swan saw a dark form under the water, but before it could lift out its head, Tarka had bitten on to its neck. Heavily its wings beat the water. Every curlew on the sandbank cried in a long uprising whistle, *cu-u-ur-leek*, *cur-r-r-leek*, and the alarm flew up and down the estuary as fast as sound travelled. The treble whistle of the redshank was piped from shore to shore, the ring plover sped over the water, turning and wheeling as one bird. Old Nog cried *Kra-r-rk*! Wind from the swan's wings scalloped the water and scattered the spray, and one struck Tarka a blow that made him float slowly away. But Greymuzzle hung to the swan's foot, even when her rudder was nearly out of the water as she was dragged along. The swan trumpeted afar its anger and fear . . .

Across the pull of the tide, among the grating ice-floes, the otters took the swan, whose flappings were getting feeble as the death-fear grew less. Tarka had bitten the artery in the neck. When the otters rested, the bird lay quiet on the water. It heard the wings of its brethren beating out the flying song of swans, *Hompa*, *hompa*, *hompa*, high and remote in the night. It flapped thrice and died.

From *Tarka the Otter*
Henry Williamson

Cormorants

The sea has it this way: if you see
Cormorants, they are the pattern for the eye.
In the sky, on the rocks, in the water, shags!
To think of them every way: I see them, oily rags
Flung starboard from some tramp and washed
On to rocks, flung up by the waves, squashed
Into sock-shapes with the foot up; sooty birds
Wearing white, but not foam-white; swearing not
    words,
But blaspheming with swastika-gesture, wing-hinge
    to nose;
Ugly grotesqueries, all in a shag's pose.
And beautifully ugly for their being shags,
Not partly swans. When the eye searches for rags,
It does not seek muslin, white satin; nor,
For its purpose, does the sea adorn shags more.

John Blight

The Whale

whale

must swim by the side of
the ship. If I take a dip
I can ride safe back on his
broad blue head. Whale is
the biggest, are you not,
vast whale? In a storm you
can shelter the ship from the
waves. I will feed you for this
with plenty of plankton.

I am partial to plankton. I will
swim by your side. Yes, I will swim
by the ark's hind rim
and soothe the poor beasts who are sick.

From *Noah's Journey*
George Macbeth

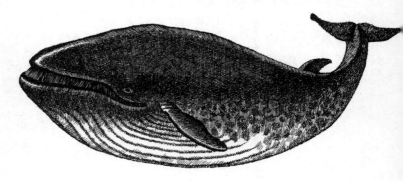

Seal

See how he dives
From the rocks with a zoom!
See how he darts
Through his watery room
Past crabs and eels
And green seaweed,
Past fluffs of sandy
Minnow feed!
See how he swims
With a swerve and a twist,
A flip of the flipper,
A flick of the wrist!
Quicksilver-quick,
Softer than spray,
Down he plunges
And sweeps away;
Before you can think,
Before you can utter
Words like "Dill pickle"
Or "Apple butter,"
Back up he swims
Past sting-ray and shark,
Out with a zoom,
A whoop, a bark;

Before you can say
Whatever you wish,
He plops at your side
With a mouthful of fish!

William Jay Smith

At Play with Seals

Floating in the water, Dumas closely studied the
seals' diving technique. They closed their nostrils,
turned on their sides, caressed the water with their
cheeks, and vanished without a splash. Dumas, the
most 'liquid' of us, looked awkward as he tried to
copy them. A heavy swell laboured on the rocks,
shaking up muddy water full of nettling micro-organ-
isms and stinging jellyfish, but Didi and Philippe were
too absorbed in their swimming lesson to notice the
inconveniences. The seals seemed to enjoy the visit of
the amateurs. A big bull quietly submerged behind
Tailliez and popped up to surprise him, face to face.

Philippe cupped his hand and splashed the seal in the face. The seal puffed and blew like a small boy. Dumas shook with laughter. The laugh turned to a shout. He rolled over and thrust his mask into the water. He saw the departing rump of a seal which had sneaked up and tickled his back with its whiskers.

From *The Silent World*
J. Y. Cousteau

Fishing Harbour Towards Evening

Slashed clouds leak gold. Along the slurping wharf
The snugged boats creak and seesaw. Round the
    masts

Abrasive squalls flake seagulls off the sky:
Choppy with wings the rapids of shrill sound.

Wrapt in spliced airs of fish and tar,
Light wincing on their knives, the clockwork men

Incise and scoop the oily pouches, flip
The soft guts overboard with blood-wet fingers.

Among three rhythms the slapping silver turns
To polished icy marble upon the deck.

Richard Kell

UNDER THE WATER

Grim and Gloomy

Oh, grim and gloomy,
So grim and gloomy
Are the caves beneath the sea.
Oh, rare but roomy
And bare and boomy,
Those salt sea caverns be.

Oh, slim and slimy
Or grey and grimy
Are the animals of the sea.
Salt and oozy
And safe and snoozy
The caves where those animals be.

Hark to the shuffling,
Huge and snuffling,
Ravenous, cavernous, great sea-beasts!
But fair and fabulous,
Tintinnabulous,
Gay and fabulous are their feasts.

Ah, but the queen of the sea,
The querulous, perilous sea!
How the curls of her tresses
The pearls on her dresses,
Sway and swirl in the waves,
How sweet ring-a-rosy
Her bower in the deep-sea caves!

Oh, rare but roomy
And bare and boomy
Those caverns under the sea,
And grave and grandiose,
Safe and sandiose
The dens of her denizens be.

James Reeves

An Enchanted Garden

I shall never forget my surprise and delight on first
beholding the bottom of the sea . . . The water within
the reef was as calm as a pond; and, as there was no
wind, it was quite clear, from the surface to the
bottom, so that we could see down easily even at a
depth of twenty or thirty yards. When Jack and I
dived into shallower water, we expected to have found
sand and stones, instead of which we found ourselves
in what appeared really to be an enchanted garden.
The whole of the bottom of the lagoon, as we called

the calm water within the reef, was covered with coral of every shape, size and hue. Some portions were formed like large mushrooms; others appeared like the brain of a man, having stalks or necks attached to them; but the most common kind was a species of branching coral, and some portions were of a lovely pale pink colour, others were pure white. Among this there grew large quantities of sea-weed of the richest hues imaginable, and of the most graceful forms; while innumerable fishes – blue, red, yellow, green and striped – sported in and out among the flower-beds of this submarine garden.

From *The Coral Island*
R. M. Ballantyne

Full Fathom Five

Full fathom five thy father lies:
   Of his bones are coral made;
Those are pearls that were his eyes:
   Nothing of him that doth fade,
But doth suffer a sea-change
Into something rich and strange.
Sea-nymphs hourly ring his knell:
   Ding-dong.
   Hark! now I hear them –
     Ding-dong, bell!

William Shakespeare

The Diver

I would like to dive
Down
Into this still pool
Where the rocks at the bottom are safely deep,

Into the green
Of the water seen from within,
A strange light
Streaming past my eyes –

Things hostile,
You cannot stay here, they seem to say;
The rocks, slime-covered, the undulating
Fronds of weeds –

And drift slowly
Among the cooler zones;
Then, upward turning,
Break from the green glimmer

Into the light,
White and ordinary of the day,
And the mild air,
With the breeze and the comfortable shore.

W. W. E. Ross

The Pool in the Rock

In this water, clear as air,
Lurks a lobster in its lair.
Rock-bound weed sways out and in,
Coral-red, and bottle-green.
Wondrous pale anemones
Stir like flowers in a breeze:
Fluted scallop, whelk in shell,
And the prowling mackerel.
Winged with snow the sea-mews ride
The brine-keen wind; and far and wide
Sounds on the hollow thunder of the tide.

Walter de la Mare